Music About The Seasons

CONTENTS

Learning Songs

The Reason For Each Season 3
Spring Seeds 9
Summer Bees 14
Autumn Lights 18
A Winter Welcome 22
Will There Be A Spring? 27

Supplementary Songs

The Days Of The Months 31
Spring, Spring, Spring! 32
Cuckoo Waltz 37
Summertime (Lullaby) – from *Porgy And Bess* 40
The Green Leaves Of Summer 42
Summer Holiday 45
September Song 48
A Winter's Tale 51
The Twelve Days Of Christmas 54

Series Editor: Mark Mumford

Music arranged and processed by Barnes Music Engraving Ltd
East Sussex TN22 4HA, England

Cover Design by Headline Publicity Ltd, Chelmsford, Essex

Published 1995

INTRODUCTION

The Music About Us series aims to provide an essential library of topical resource material for Key Stage One and Key Stage Two pupils. The songs, together with the accompanying teaching ideas, are ideal for creating an immediate musical environment.

The Learning Songs are original, informative and fun to sing and perform. They provide thematic links to other subjects within the National Curriculum and will prove ideal for cross-curricular topic or project work. The use of the songs, and indeed much of the material in this series, will be dependent upon the age and ability of the children. In most cases however, the material is flexible enough to be adapted to deal with a number of requirements, thus providing the teacher with an ideal resource collection to 'dip into'.

Teaching Ideas provide initial suggestions for using the learning songs. They offer a variety of ways in which the songs may be performed, sometimes including ideas for actions, movement games and instrumental accompaniments. These suggestions can be combined to form a complete performance or simply selected to help with musical response and understanding. Their use will be dependent on key stage requirements.

The Musical Discussion notes offer further ideas and suggestions for exploring musical concepts. They provide initial points of discussion, sometimes concentrating on one specific musical element. There are many ways of developing these points but primarily they act as a basis for stimulating further work.

The Topical Discussion notes provide a series of leads enabling further exploration of the thematic content of the song. These are particularly useful for cross-curricular links within the National Curriculum, when applicable to the relevant key stage.

The Supplementary Song section offers a variety of songs, many of which may be well known. These songs may prove suitable for a number of uses, but as thematic material they can be used simply for singing. However, they can be developed by adding percussion accompaniments, actions etc.

Whether it is used to sing and learn about ourselves, how we live and the world around us, or as a basis for stimulating musical activity, the *Music About Us* series will undoubtedly prove a useful resource for music making in the classroom.

The Reason For Each Season

Words and Music by
Carrie Morrow

C7 F C7 F B♭ F
mea - sure lit - tle shoots, each day they grow. Re - cord the wind with a
com - pare au - tumn col - ours all a - round. List fruits and pods, and some
B♭ F G7 C G C7
com - pass and a vane, put out a jug to catch spring rain.
nuts, seeds and wings, call the dis - play, 'Our Au - tumn Things'!
Gm 3fr C7
Lis - ten to the song - birds call - ing for a mate. Hide with a tape re - cord - er,
Hi - ber - nat - ing crea - tures, some will build a store, search in the li - bra - ry to
F C7 F B♭ F B♭ F
keep still, wait. A grow - ing chart for tad - poles, now they have back legs, and
find out more. The au - tumn winds are strong now, so it is all right to

C
F
F/C
C7
F
F
just for fun, in spring, de - co - rate Eas - ter eggs. We're find - ing out the rea - son
say NO to your home - work, and go fly a kite! We're
C7
F
C7
for each sea - son, we're no - tic - ing the chan - ges as the earth turns round.
F
B♭
C7
F
This is what we've found.
2. On the ther - mo - me - ter,
4. Mea - sure the temp - era - ture,
Gm
3fr
C7
F
C7
F
how ma - ny de - grees? Count - ing col - oured flo - wers, and the sum - mer trees.
freez - ing or be - low, look for hea - vy clouds, they threat - en win - ter snow.

B♭ F B♭ F G7 C G C7
Guess ev - ery flo - wer sim - ply by the smell, sort out the beach hunt, group each shell.
Find bro - ken twigs, with buds shut up so tight, show on a graph the hours of light.
Gm C7
Tick the in - sect chart if at all you see but - ter - fly, a dra - gon - fly, or
Search for ev - er - greens; there's a hol - ly bush, when the fro - zen snow melts, it
F C7 F B♭ F B♭ F
buzz - ing bee. In this love - ly wea - ther, go and have some fun, so
turns to slush. Tal - ly all the small birds peck - ing at our bread, now
C F 1. F/C C7 F 2. F/C C7 F
pack your work a - way, read a book in the sun. We're snow - man in - stead!
for - get find - ing out, build a

We're finding out the reason for each season,
We're noticing the changes as the earth turns round.
This is what we've found.

1 Look at the buds as colours start to show,
Measure little shoots, each day they grow.
Record the wind with a compass and a vane,
Put out a jug to catch spring rain.
Listen to the songbirds calling for a mate.
Hide with a tape recorder, keep still, wait.
A growing chart for tadpoles, now they have back legs,
And just for fun, in spring, decorate Easter eggs.
We're finding out . . .

2 On the thermometer, how many degrees?
Counting coloured flowers, and the summer trees.
Guess every flower simply by the smell,
Sort out the beach hunt, group each shell.
Tick the insect chart if at all you see
Butterfly, a dragonfly, or buzzing bee.
In this lovely weather, go and have some fun,
So pack your work away, read a book in the sun.
We're finding out . . .

3 Collect conkers, fallen to the ground,
Compare autumn colours all around.
List fruits and pods, and some nuts, seeds and wings,
Call the display 'Our Autumn Things'!
Hibernating creatures, some will build a store,
Search in the library to find out more.
The autumn winds are strong now, so it is all right
To say NO to your homework, and go fly a kite!
We're finding out . . .

4 Measure the temperature, freezing or below,
Look for heavy clouds, they threaten winter snow.
Find broken twigs, with buds shut up so tight,
Show on a graph the hours of light.
Search for evergreens; there's a holly bush,
When the frozen snow melts, it turns to slush.
Tally all the small birds pecking at our bread,
Now forget finding out, build a snowman instead!
We're finding out . . .

TEACHING IDEAS

A song that highlights some of the characteristics of the seasons, with some suggestions for investigating them further.

Actions

Look at the buds – Clench fist
Measure little shoots – Let fingers poke out one by one
Compass and weather vane – Point north, east, west and south
Put out a jug – Cup hands together
Listen to song-birds – Make a bird shape with two hands
Keep still, wait – Put finger on lip – make a sssh sound
Growing chart for tadpoles – Quick swishing movements with hand
Decorate Easter eggs – Draw an egg shape in the air

Ask the children to invent actions for the other verses.

Accompaniments

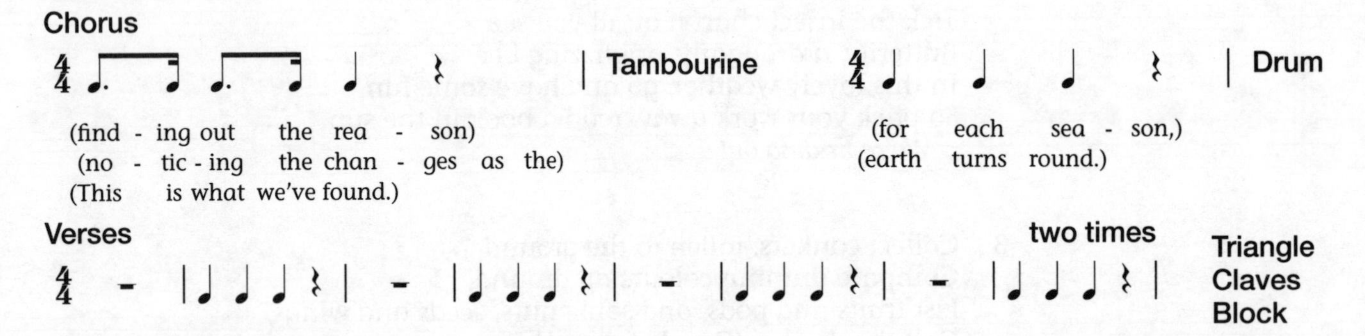

Musical Discussion

Discuss different types of bird sound. Ask the children to record different types of bird song. Compare the differences. Can the children imitate the sounds? Are there long or short sounds? Are some sounds higher in pitch than others? Ask the children to arrange the sounds in order from high to low. Which percussion instruments best imitate bird sounds and why?

Listen to excerpts from Vivaldi's 'Four Seasons' and discuss the changes of mood between each of the seasons.

Topical Discussion

Find a picture or photograph which portrays either a garden or woodland scene. Ask the children to paint a picture of the same scene in a different season. Can they think of sounds to match the different settings? Think about the weather and insect life particularly. How do the pictures contrast in colour? How do they contrast in sound?

Spring Seeds

A7
Dm
C
F
G
down in the earth. Wait for the spring-time, and all its new
fresh, wet and green. Sho - wers and warm air, now blos - soms are
C
B♭
F/A
Gm7
3fr
C7
F
C7
F/A
birth. Lit - tle seed, lit - tle seed, one day you'll be a tall
seen.
mf
B♭
F/C
C7
F
B♭
F
strong sy - ca - more tree. Twirl - ing, twirl - ing, round and round,
C7/E
C7
F
F7
B♭
round and round, he - li - cop - ter to the ground. Whir - ring,

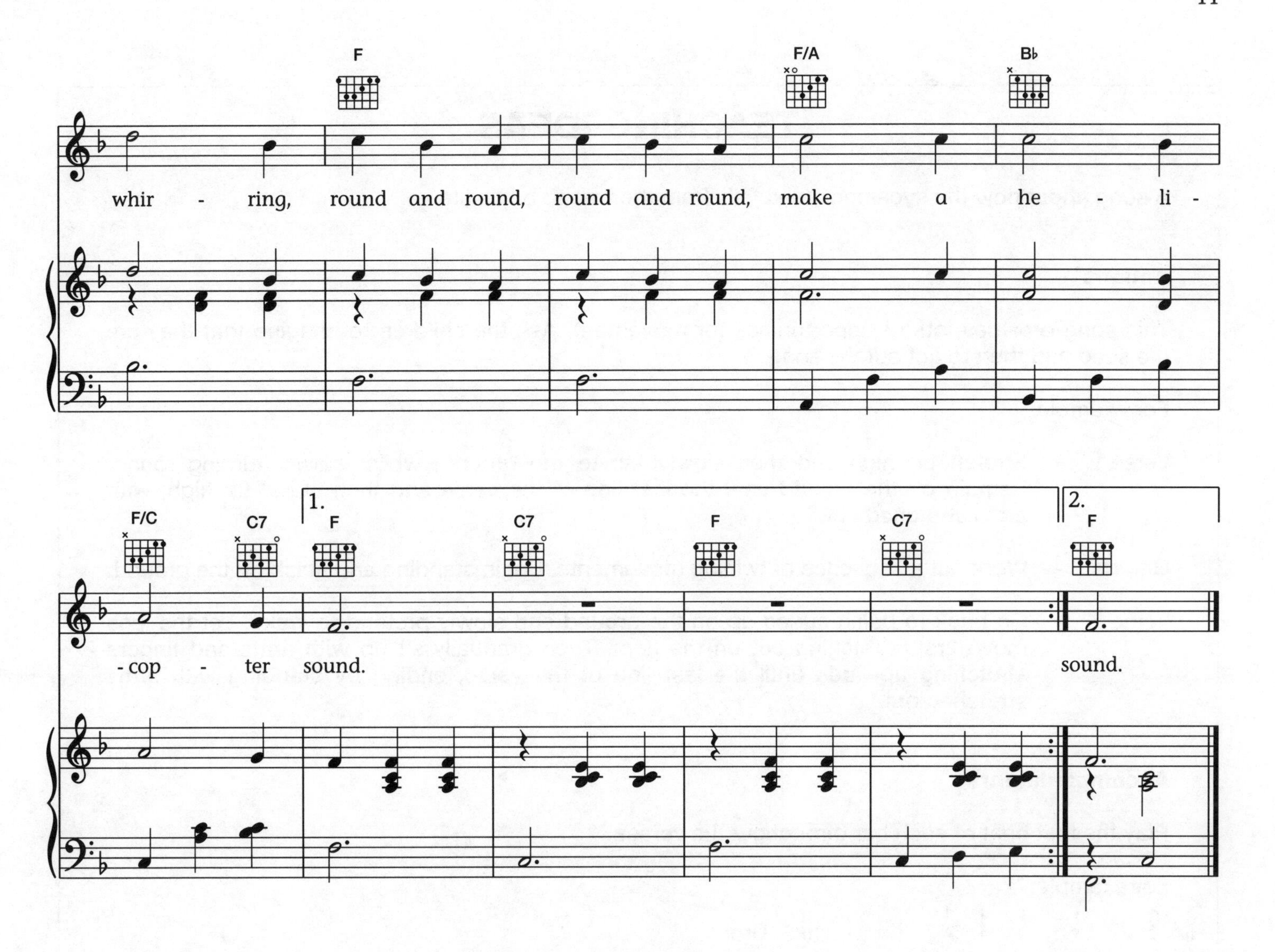

1 Sycamore seeds, high up in the tree,
Jump together, after three.
Spin, whirl, round and round twirl,
Round and round twirl, spin, whirl.
Hide from cold winter, deep down in the earth.
Wait for the springtime, and all its new birth,
Little seed, little seed, one day you'll be
A tall strong sycamore tree.

Twirling, twirling, round and round, round and round,
Helicopter to the ground.
Whirring, whirring, round and round, round and round,
Make a helicopter sound.

2 Sycamore seeds, with long creeping roots,
All around are sycamore shoots.
Dance, sing, here is the spring,
Here is the spring, dance, sing.
Wake to a new world, all fresh wet and green.
Showers and warm air, now blossoms are seen,
Little seed, little seed, one day you'll be
A tall strong sycamore tree.
Twirling, twirling . . .

TEACHING IDEAS

A song about how the sycamore seed falls from the tree to begin life.

Actions

This song provides lots of opportunities for movement. Ask the children to imagine that they are the seed and then to act out the song.

For example:

Verse 1 – Stretch up high and then slowly fall to the ground, whilst slowly turning round. Remain on the ground until the last line of the verse and then stand up high, with arms stretched out.

Chorus – Work out a sequence of twirling movements. Begin standing and finish on the ground.

Verse 2 – Go back to being curled up on the ground and slowly pretend to wake. Let the legs move first, stretching out on the floor. Then gradually sit up with arms and fingers stretching upwards until the last line of the verse, ending by standing with arms stretched out.

Accompaniments

Play the first beat of each bar throughout the verses.

For example:

Chorus

Glockenspiels or Recorders

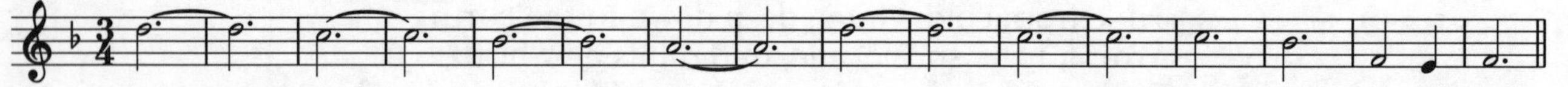

Musical Discussion

Discuss getting gradually higher and lower in pitch. Ask the children to arrange a group of percussion instruments in a row, tuned and untuned, with the lowest sounding ones first. Divide the children into two groups. Ask one group to gradually play through the percussion sounds and the other to respond by imitating a seed growing into a tree. Alternatively, ask the whole class to respond to the rising notes of a scale, played on a piano.

Discuss growing in relation to musical texture. Divide the children into five groups. Give each group a rhythmic pattern. After the first group have played their pattern four times, the second group should enter, and so on.

For example:

The children should also be encouraged to start quietly, gradually getting louder towards the end of the exercise. Talk about how the texture of the music changed. The words may help the children grasp the rhythm.

Encourage the children to improvise an answer to the 'little seed' rhythm found in the song.

For example:

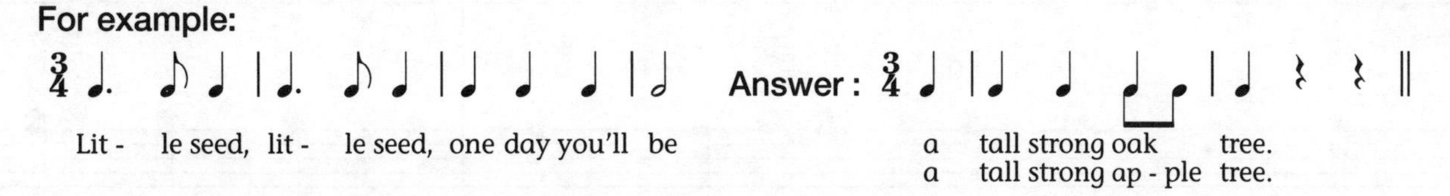

They can also try clapping the musical replies.

Ask the children to collect different types of seeds. *Caution: some might be poisonous.* It may be a good idea to tell them which seeds to collect. Using an assortment of containers, try making some musical shakers. Discuss the different types of sounds.

Topical Discussion

Ask the children to name the months we associate with spring in this country. Spring is a time when all sorts of life forms begin to grow, and when many creatures give birth to their young. Discuss and list some of the characteristics of spring, including the new life that appears around us. Why do seeds begin to grow in the springtime? What does 'germination' mean? Sycamore seeds are shaped so that they fall away from the tree and grow. Find out how other plants disperse their seeds e.g. strawberry seeds eaten by birds, poppy seeds spread by the wind, etc.

Collect different seeds. What will they change into? Compare the different sizes, colour and texture. Some plants multiply without seeds. Can the children think of any examples? Why do animals and birds have their young in springtime?

Find pictures that represent spring and create a spring collage.

Summer Bees

Words and Music by
Carrie Morrow

A Bb/Ab G A7 D A7
Flo - wers, love - ly col - ours bright, the bees and in - sects all de - light.
Pol - len's what a flo - wer needs to grow next year's lit - tle seeds.
D A D A G A D
Bu - sy, buz - zy, bu - sy, buz - zy, bees, bees, dodg - ing in and out, and round the
G A7 G D/F# Em7 A
sum - mer trees. In and out the flo - wers, through the long, hot hours, a
D A D A7 D A7 D
1. 2.
bu - sy sum - mer bee, mak - ing hon - ey for tea. hon - ey for tea.

1 All around the children play,
Busy bees at work all day.
Gardens, parks are so much fun,
Buzzing in the summer sun.
Look down at the flower bed,
Petals orange, white and red.
Flowers, lovely colours bright,
The bees and insects all delight.

Busy buzzy, busy buzzy, bees, bees,
Dodging in and out, and round the summer trees.
In and out the flowers, through the long, hot hours,
A busy summer bee, making honey for tea.

2 Nectar, sugary and sweet,
Sticky food for bees to eat.
Sticky, with a sweet, sweet smell,
And a lovely taste as well.
Please bees, do you realize,
You help the flowers fertilize?
Pollen's what a flower needs
To grow next year's little seeds.
Busy buzzy . . .

TEACHING IDEAS

A look at summer through the work of bees.

Accompaniments

Verses

Claves, Guiro, etc.

4/4 Repeat throughout verse
Encourage the children to play short (*staccato*) sounds

Chorus

Drum, Tambourine, etc.

4/4 Repeat throughout chorus

Vocal bee sounds (*bzzzz*) can be added during the chorus on the words 'buzzy' and 'bees'.

Verses – Tuned percussion

Xylophone and Glockenspiel

Ensure that the words 'busy' and 'buzzy' are pronounced correctly.

Musical Discussion

Discuss long and short sounds. Can the children give some vocal examples? Talk about short and long words. What is the longest word that the children know? Compare the two untuned percussion accompaniments in the song. How do the children control the instruments to make the sounds shorter? Play the accompaniments again, and encourage the children to take steps in time with the rhythms.

For example:

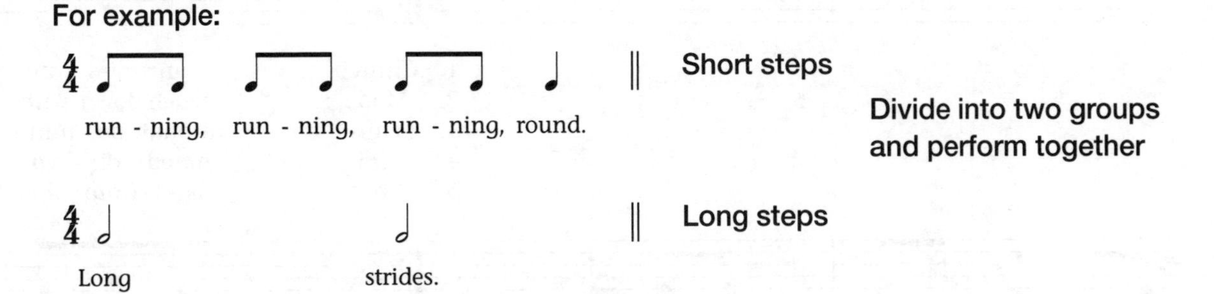

Introduce a walking rhythm to represent crotchets.

Use flower symbols to represent long and short sounds.

For example:

Using flashcards, ask the children to sing and clap the rhythms. Ask the children to compose their own pattern using flower symbols to represent long and short sounds, This idea can be expanded by drawing the flowers on a large piece of paper arranging the flowers at different heights. The higher a flower – the higher the sound. The children decide which sounds will match the different flowers. Using dotted lines, they can make up a journey of a bee visiting different flowers. When they have decided on the bee's journey, they can then perform their composition, according to the bee's route.

For example:

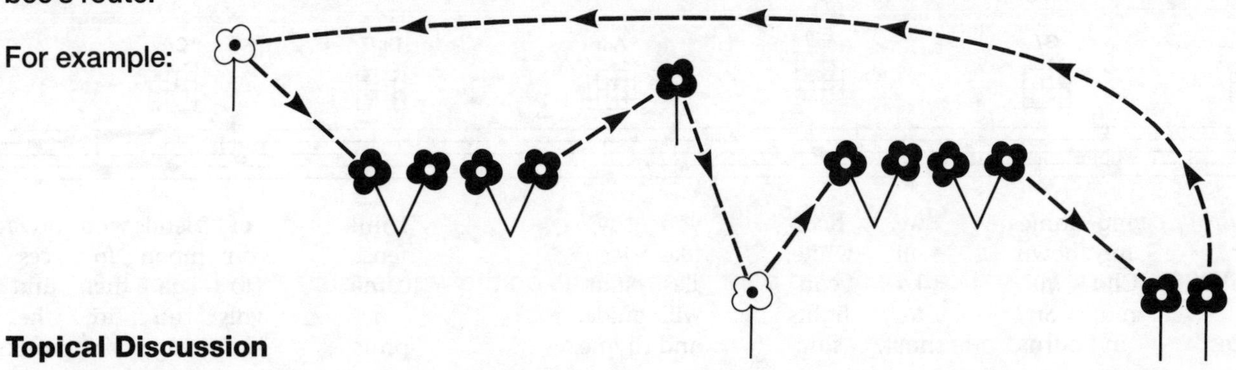

Topical Discussion

Which months would the children include in the summer season? What attracts bees and insects to flowers? How do bees and insects help flowers to fertilise? Have the children ever eaten honey? What fruits and vegetables do the children associate with summer? Discuss the weather in summer. What do the children do in the summer holidays? Discuss the effects of summer, e.g. how we feel in hot weather. Talk about the different smelling flowers. What different clothes do we wear? Talk about summer colours in comparison to those of winter, particularly in the countryside.

Autumn Lights

Words and Music by
Carrie Morrow

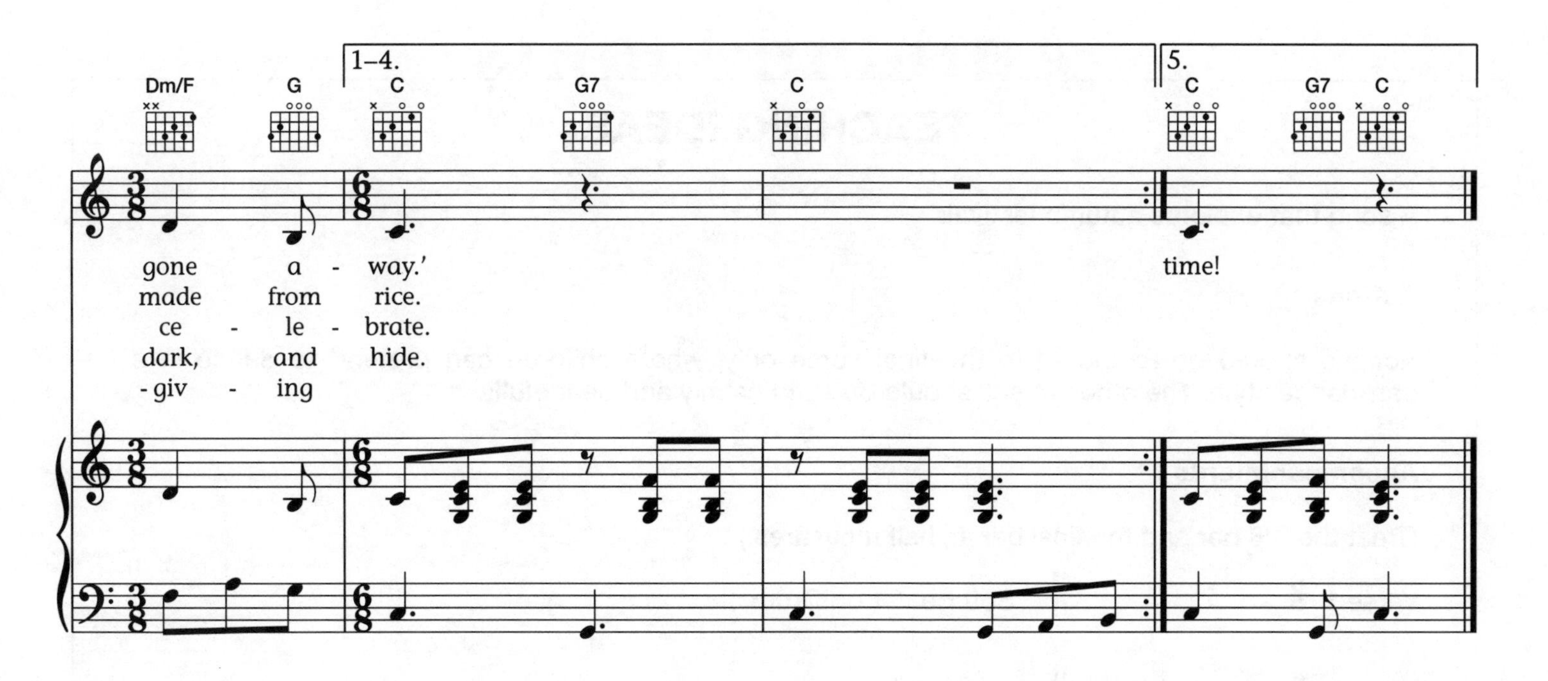

1 Church candles are burning bright,
Keeping watch on All Souls' Night
Bowing flames, we hear you say,
'Think of friends who have gone away.'

2 Moon reach down with silver beams,
Stronger in the dark it seems,
Staring down all white, like ice,
Feast on moon faces made from rice.

3 Fires through autumn nights will blaze,
Bravely burn through winter days,
Count Chanuka candles, eight,
Come together, and celebrate.

4 Coloured diva lights at home,
Lakshmi, she will surely come,
Rama, Sita, lights will guide,
Rivals run to the dark, and hide.

5 Cornlight from the fields of gold,
Harvest crops for winter's cold,
Dance in barns, shout, sing and rhyme,
Praises ring, it's thanksgiving time!

TEACHING IDEAS

A song that explores autumn festivals.

Actions

Actions should be restricted to the final verse only, where children can pretend to dance in a barndance style. The other verses should be sung calmly and peacefully.

Accompaniments

(Treat the 3/8 bar and the final bar as half measures.)

Verse 1 6/8 ♩. ♩. :‖ Soft beater on Drum

Verse 2 6/8 ♩ ♪ ♩ ♪ :‖ Soft beater on Cymbal

Verse 3 6/8 ♩. ♫♪ :‖ Triangle

Verse 4 6/8 ♫♪ ♩ ♪ :‖ Indian Bells

Verse 5 – Combine all or some of the rhythms, use clapping or stamping as well.

Musical Discussion

Invent or ask the children to invent short stories or verse, describing an autumn scene. Then ask them to add sound effects to accompany what happens in the story.

For example:

The Little Leaf

The wind whistled and twirled around,	*(soft blowing on recorders/whistles)*
Accompanied by a tapping sound,	*(short sharp taps with sticks or claves)*
Which was of course the fall of rain,	*(shakers and tambourines)*
As it lashed upon the window pane.	
Just outside in our front garden,	
Stood a tall tree creaking and barren,	*(creaking sounds with voice)*
But clinging to the highest branch,	*(glissando low to high on glockenspiels)*
Was a little leaf in crazy dance.	*(tambourines)*
All of a sudden lightning flashed and thunder clashed,	*(cymbal and drums)*
And a surge of wind forced the leaf to become detached,	*(blowing sounds, snap a twig)*
Down and down, round and round,	
Gently falling to the ground.	*(one strike of a triangle as the leaf lands on the ground)*

(M.M.)

Topical Discussion

Why do the days become colder and darker in autumn? Do all parts of the world have the same seasonal patterns? Find out more about festivals of light in different religions and in different cultural traditions.

Festival of Light in Autumn

Christians celebrate All Souls' Day on 2nd November. They say prayers and light candles for friends and family who have died. Even before Christian times, people lit fires to honour spirits. The tradition still continues each year at Hallowe'en.

Many religions have festivals at the time of a new moon. In China, there is a festival of the Autumn Moon. People feast and eat little rice cakes shaped like a full moon.

In autumn, the sun seems to be getting weaker. Many traditional festivals involve lighting fires to give the sun more power. Chanukah is a Jewish festival which lasts for eight days. Each day, one candle is lit on a candlestick with eight branches.

Diwali is a festival of light celebrated by Hindus and Sikhs. Hindus honour Lakshmi, the goddess of good fortune, and they decorate their homes with small lamps called divas. Hindus also celebrate Dessehra in autumn. Stories may be told about how Sita and Prince Rama defeated a demon.

Many cultures and religions have a Harvest Festival to celebrate a successful year's farming. Many people give thanks for the sun, the rain, and all the fruits of the earth.

A Winter Welcome

Words and Music by
Carrie Morrow

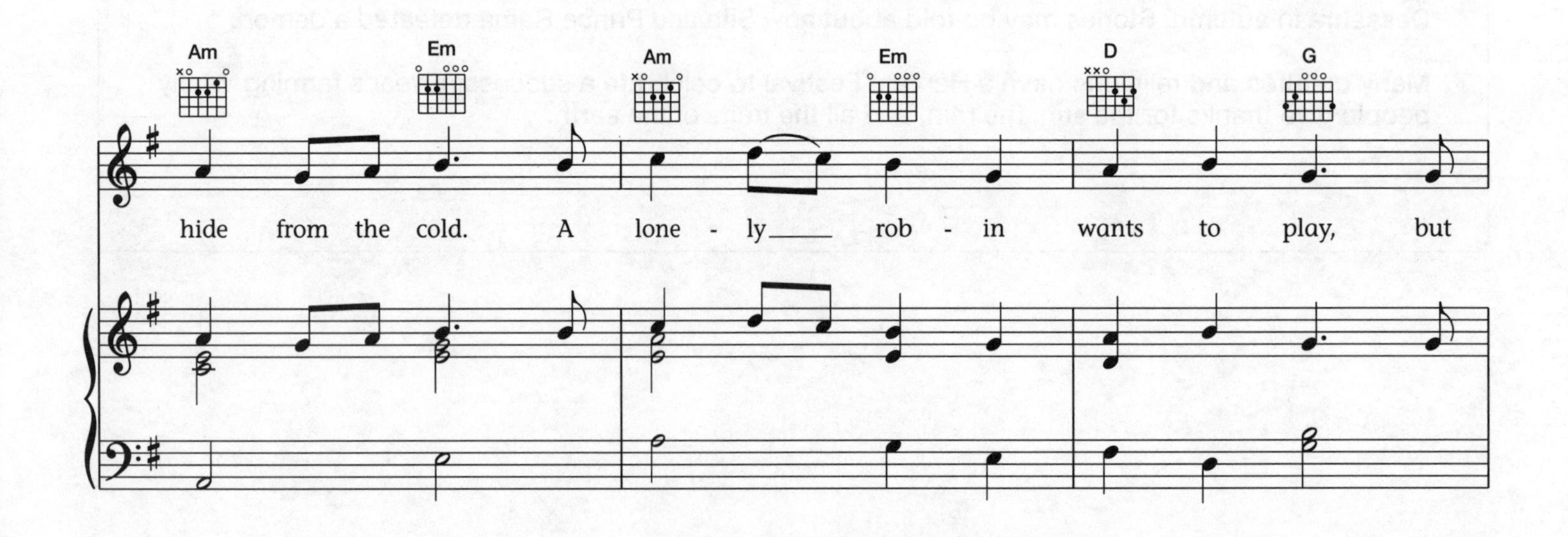

D G C G/B A7 D C C/E
sky so bright, sprink-ling seeds of sil-ver light. Bells, bells,
G C G/B D
joy-ful-ly ring, wel-com-ing a new born king.
Em C G Bm C
In the dark-est win-ter still be-lieve to-night, to-night is
D7 G B Em
Christ-mas Eve. Trees creak,

Bm Em Am Em
bare and old, ti - ny crea - tures hide from the cold. A
Am Em D G Em
lone - ly rob - in wants to play, but all the oth - er birds have
Bm Em C G D G
gone a - way. 2. Dra - gon, dra - gon, win - ter will fear,
C G/B A7 D C C/E G
danc - ing wel - come the New Year. Fire - crack - er, fire - crack - er, cym - bal and gong,

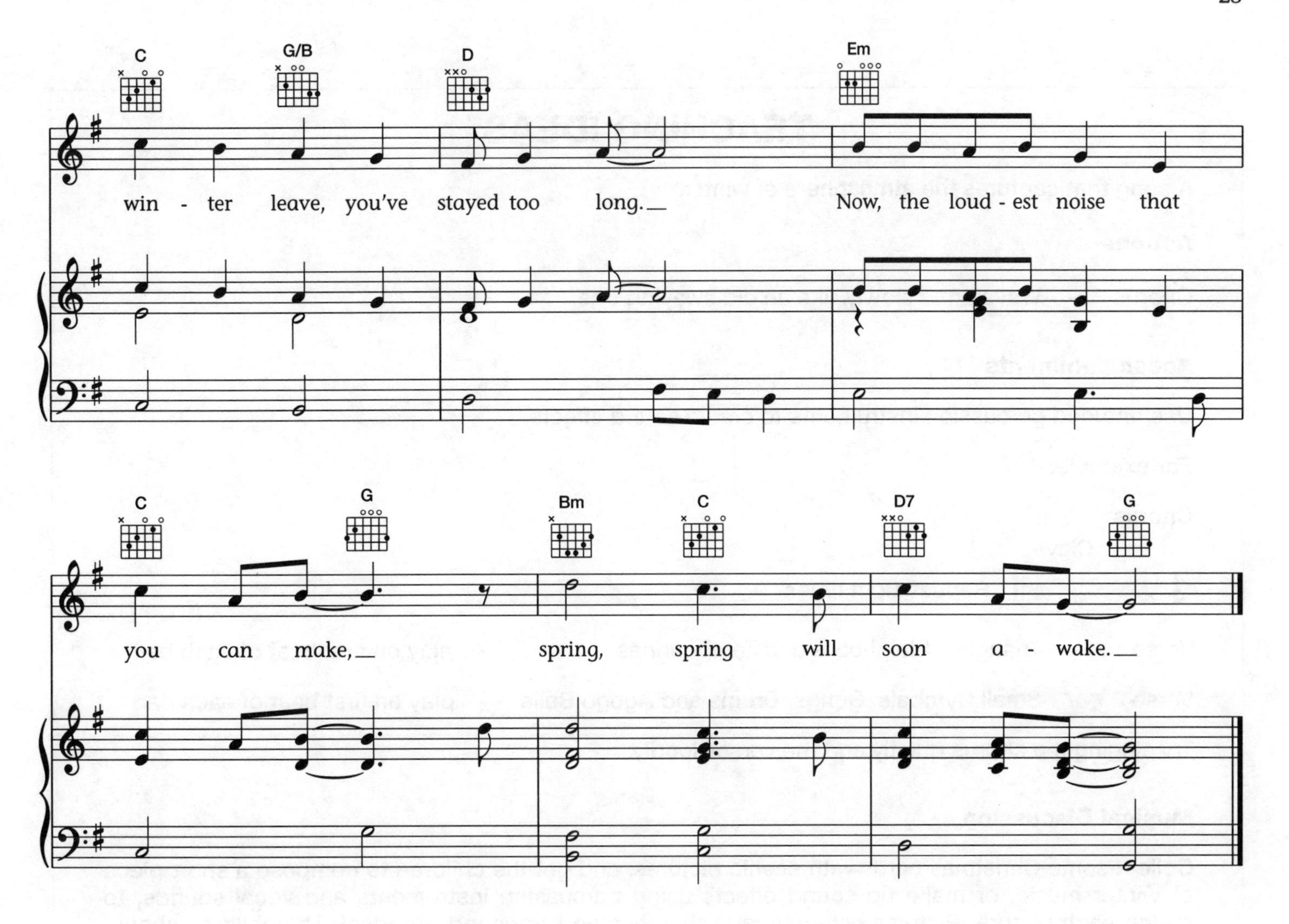

1 Star, star in the sky so bright,
Sprinkling seeds of silver light,
Bells, bells, joyfully ring,
Welcoming a new born king.
In the darkest winter, still believe,
Tonight, tonight is Christmas Eve.

Trees creak, bare and old,
Tiny creatures hide from the cold.
A lonely robin wants to play,
But all the other birds have gone away.

2 Dragon, dragon winter will fear,
Dancing welcome the New Year.
Firecracker, firecracker, cymbal and gong,
Winter leave, you've stayed too long.
Now the loudest noise that you can make,
Spring, spring will soon awake.
Trees creak . . .

TEACHING IDEAS

A song that captures the atmosphere of winter.

Actions

Chorus – Wave arms slowly, like an old swaying tree.

Accompaniments

Use untuned percussion instruments to create sound effects.

For example:

Chorus

Claves

Repeat eight times

Verse 1 – Triangles, Sleighbells and Tambourines – play on first beat of each bar.

Verse 2 – Small Cymbals, Gongs, Drums and Agogo Bells – play on first beat of each bar.

Try singing the chorus quietly and the verses loudly.

Musical Discussion

Collect some Christmas cards with scenic pictures, and get the children to compose a short piece of winter music, or make up sound effects using percussion instruments and vocal sounds, to match each picture. Pictures with animals, churches and transport are ideal. The children should perform their results to each other. Encourage them also to appraise each other's performance by asking questions such as: Which type of sounds were used? Were different levels of dynamics used? How did the piece begin, and how did it end?

Pick out two-bar musical patterns from the song and play simple rhythmic echo games.

For example:

Ask the children to clap an echo and then repeat on percussion instruments.

Divide the children into groups and give each group their own pattern to memorise, with words. Bring the groups together and arrange so as to sing the two-bar patterns as an accumulative piece.

Topical Discussion

Discuss how our living habits change in the winter, e.g. different clothes, different food, etc.

Discuss how our environment changes around us, e.g. colours, weather, landscape, etc.

Draw or paint pictures to match a Christmas song or carol. Do the children have a favourite Christmas carol or song? What is it about? Why do they like it?

Will There Be A Spring?

Words and Music by
Carrie Morrow

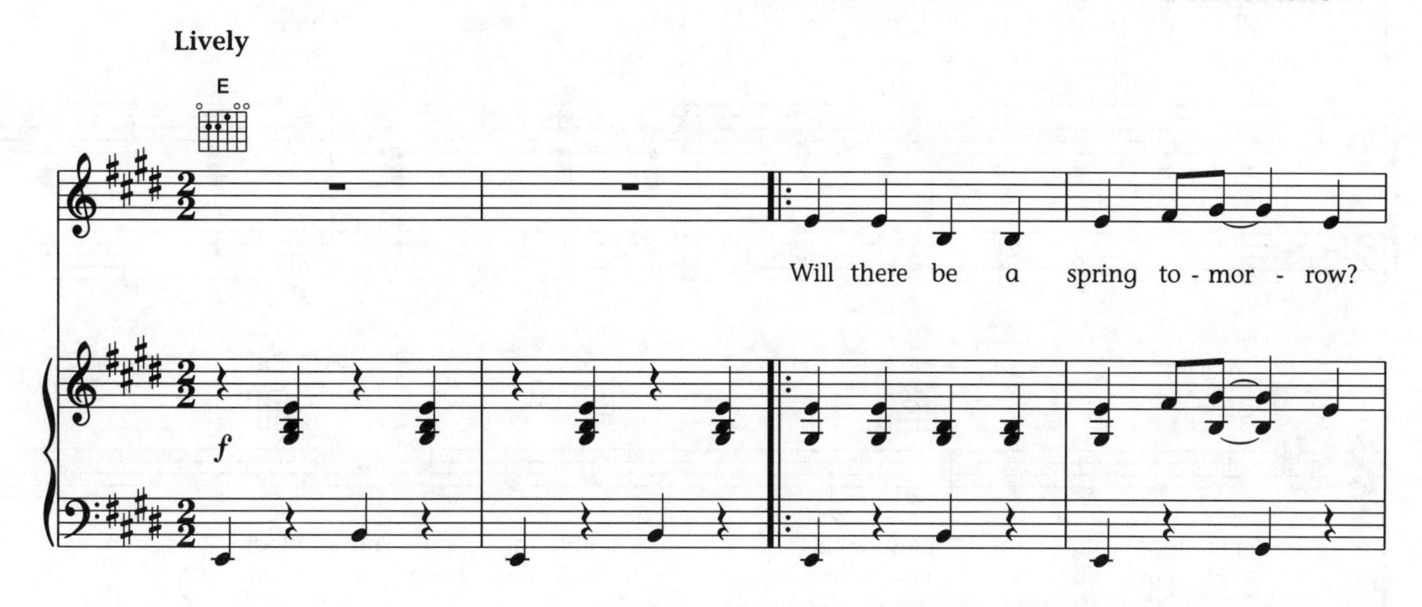

E
all a - round us no trees grow? Yee - hah!
A
E
A
E
1. Build - ings do not blos - som, build - ings do not bloom.
2. Build - ings do not lose leaves, build - ings have no fall.
F#7
B7
G#m7
4fr
C#m7
4fr
B7/F#
B7
E
In our crowd - ed ci - ty streets, na - ture finds less room.
In our crowd - ed ci - ty streets, there's no green at all.
B7
Will there be a spring to - mor - row? Will a young tree tell us so?

Will there be a spring tomorrow?
Will a young tree tell us so?
Spring or summer, autumn, winter,
How are we supposed to know,
When all around us no trees grow?

1 Buildings do not blossom,
Buildings do not bloom.
In our crowded city streets,
Nature finds less room.
Will there be . . .

2 Buildings do not lose leaves,
Buildings have no fall.
In our crowded city streets,
There's no green at all.
Will there be . . .

TEACHING IDEAS

An environmental song, highlighting the importance and the effects of the seasons.

Actions

Shrug shoulders and hold arms out on each of the questions in the chorus.

Make 1, 2, 3, 4 finger signals as each of the seasons are mentioned.

Accompaniments

Chorus

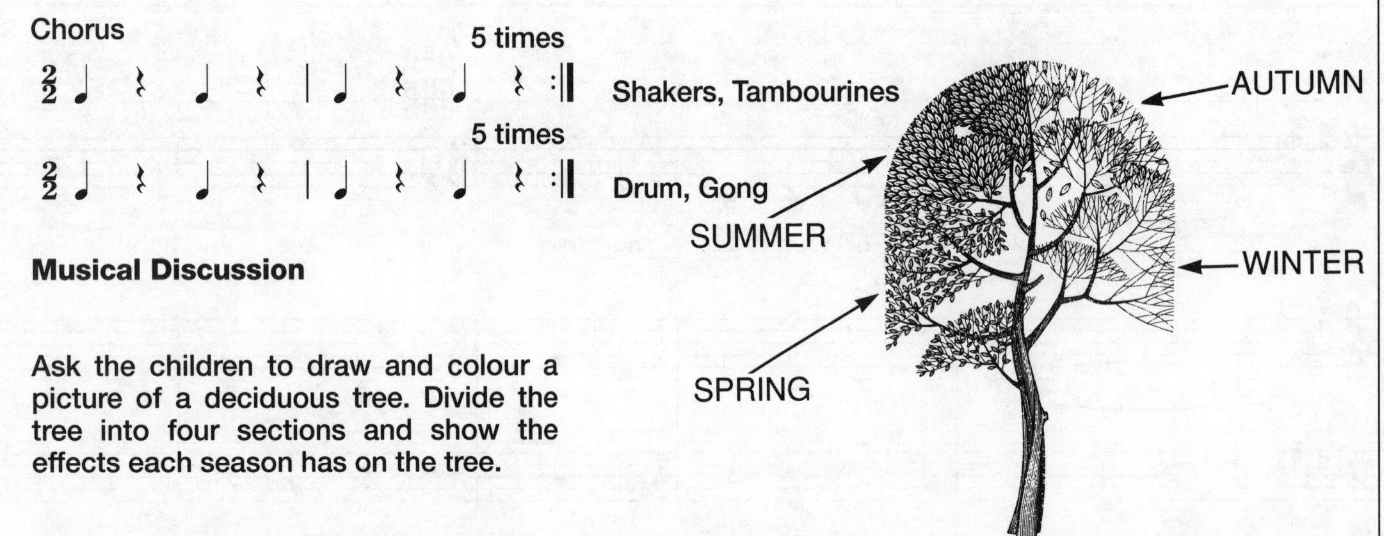

Musical Discussion

Ask the children to draw and colour a picture of a deciduous tree. Divide the tree into four sections and show the effects each season has on the tree.

Ask the children to make up a series of sound effects or short melodic patterns to accompany each season. Ask them to concentrate on creating a mood for each season.

For example:

Spring – Sounds that rise in pitch to give a sense of growing.
Imitate rain sounds.
A cuckoo sound.

Summer – Long, light sounds.
Buzzing of bees.
A grasshopper sound.
Perhaps a 'lazy' ostinato.

Autumn – The crackling sounds of a bonfire.
Wind and rustling of leaves.

Winter – Ringing of sleigh bells and hand bells.
Deep plodding sounds to portray long dark nights.

If divided into groups, each group can then perform its own season. Make a complete cycle of seasons.

Sing and listen to the supplementary songs in this book and discuss the different moods.

Topical Discussion

Discuss how some trees and plants follow a seasonal pattern. Which trees do not lose their leaves in the winter? Why is it important to conserve trees and plant more? Talk about the cutting down of trees around the world and the problems this causes. Do the children have trees in their gardens or close to their houses? What would it be like if there were no trees? Discuss some ideas for conservation.

Days Of The Months

Traditional

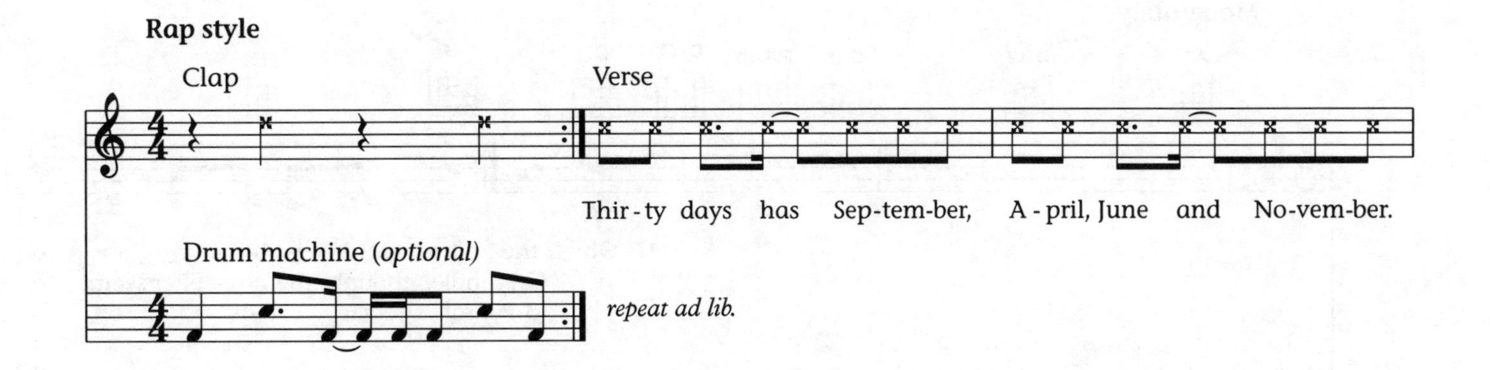

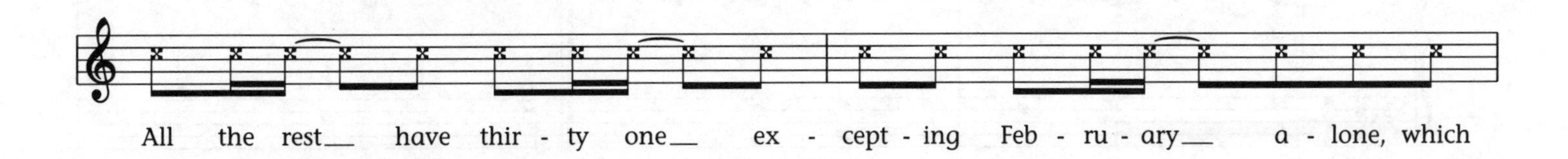

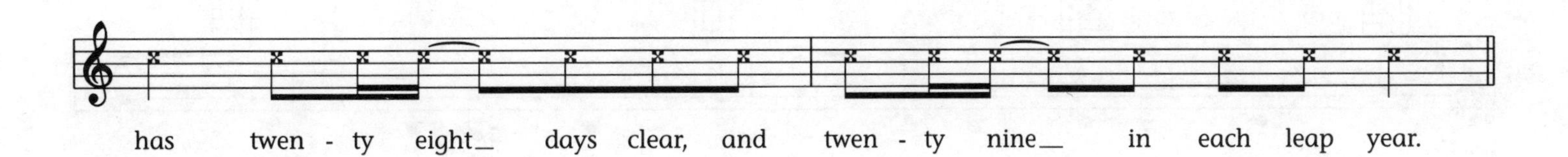

Try dividing the class into two groups: the first repeats the refrain whilst the second raps the verse at the same time.

Spring, Spring, Spring!

Words by Johnny Mercer
Music by Gene de Paul

Bm7
E7♭9
A7sus4
A7
D11
D7
her year - ly mi - ra - cle, spring, spring, spring! All the
feels that he can't e - lope, it's spring, spring, spring! Slow, but
mak - ing his wag - on fly, it's spring, spring, spring! Ev - ery
G
Em
F♯m♭5
B7♭9
hen folk are watch - in' while their men folk are scratch - in' to en -
sure - ly by the tur - tle, who's e - nor - mous - ly fer - tile, lays her
bug's snug - gled snug - gy in its own ba - by bug - gy, and in
Em
Cm/E♭
Dm7
G7
- sure the sur - vi - val of each brand new ar - ri - val.
eggs by the doz - ens, may - be some are for cou - sins,
spite of po - lic - ing, seems the tribe is in - creas - ing,
C7
F9
Bm7
E7♭9
Each nest is twit - ter - ing, they're all ba - by sit - ter - ing, it's
ev - en the ca - ta - mount is non - plussed at that a - mount, it's
'cause Mis - sus Ka - ty did once do what her ma - tey did, it's

A7 D7♭9 G Dm7 G7
spring, spring, spring! It's a bee - hive of bud - ding son and
spring, spring, spring! Ev - en out in Aus - tra - li - a, the
spring, spring, spring! Dad - dy Long Legs is stretch - ing out his
C Am7 Dm7 G7aug5 Cmaj7
daugh - ter life, ev - ery fa - mi - ly has plans in view. Ev - en
kan - ga - roos lay off but - ter - milk and all french fries. If their
creak - ing joints, and how bu - sy can a bum - ble be! Flit - ting
Em7 A7 D Bm7
down in the brook the un - der - wa - ter life is for -
off - spring are large, it might be dan - ger - ous, they've just
hi - ther and thi - ther, she keeps seek - ing joints with a
Em7 A7aug5 D7 G Em
- ev - er blow - ing bub - bles too. Ev - ery field wears a bon - net with some
got - ta keep 'em poc - ket size. Ev - en though to each rab - bit spring is
spare room and a nur - se - ry. Each co - coon has a ten - ant, so they

F#m♭5
B7♭9
Em
Cm/E♭
spring dai - sies on it, ev - en birds of a fea - ther show their
more like a ha - bit, not - with - stand - ing the fact is, they in -
hung out a pen - nant, 'Don't dis - turb, please keep wait - ing; we are
Dm7
G7
C7
F9
clothes off to - ge - ther. Sun's get - ting shi - ne - ry to
- dulge in the prac - tice. Each day is Mo - ther's Day, the
e - va - cu - a - ting. This home's my Mom - ma's, I'll soon
Bm7
E7♭9
A7
D7
spot - light the fi - ne - ry, spring, spring,
next day some oth - er's day, it's spring, spring,
have my own dom - e - cile,' it's spring, spring,
G
N.C.
1–2.
E♭7
D7
3.
D7aug5
G
spring! 2. In his
spring! 3. To it -
spring!

1 Oh, the barnyard is busy, in a regular tizzy,
And the obvious reason is because of the season.
Ma Nature's lyrical with her yearly miracle,
Spring, spring, spring!
All the hen folk are watchin' while their men folk are scratchin'
To ensure the survival of each brand new arrival.
Each nest is twittering, they're all baby-sittering,
It's spring, spring, spring!

It's a beehive of budding son and daughter life,
Every family has plans in view.
Even down in the brook the underwater life
Is forever blowing bubbles too.
Every field wears a bonnet with some spring daisies on it,
Even birds of a feather show their clothes off together.
Sun's getting shinery to spotlight the finery,
It's spring, spring, spring!

2 In his hole, though the gopher seems a bit of a loafer,
The industrious beaver puts it down to spring fever.
While there's no antelope who feels that he can't elope,
It's spring spring spring!
Slow, but surely by the turtle, who's enormously fertile,
Lays her eggs by the dozens, maybe some are for cousins,
Even the catamount is non-plussed at that amount,
It's spring, spring, spring!

Even out in Australia, the kangaroos
Lay off buttermilk and all french fries.
If their offspring are large, it might be dangerous,
They've just gotta keep 'em pocket size.
Even though to each rabbit spring is more like a habit,
Notwithstanding the fact is, they indulge in the practice.
Each day is Mother's Day, the next day some other's day,
It's spring, spring, spring!

3 To itself, each amoeba softly croons, 'Ach du lieber',
While the proud little termite feels as large as a worm might.
Old Poppa Dragonfly is making his wagon fly,
It's spring spring spring!
Every bug's snuggled snuggy in its own baby buggy,
And in spite of policing, seems the tribe is increasing,
'Cause Missus Katy did once do what her matey did,
It's spring, spring, spring!

Daddy Long Legs is stretching out his creaking joints,
And how busy can a bumble be!
Flitting hither and thither, she keeps seeking joints
With a spare room and a nursery.
Each cocoon has a tenant, so they hung out a pennant,
'Don't disturb, please keep waiting; we are evacuating.
This home's my Momma's, I'll soon have my own domecile.'
It's spring, spring, spring!

Spring has really got going in this song.
Lots of opportunities for actions and movement with maybe some painting and drawing too.

Cuckoo Waltz

Words by Alan Stranks and Ejner Westling
Music by J Emanuel Jonasson

F
-koo! Look who has sto - len my heart a - way!
B♭
Sweet is the song that I
I am as cuc - koo as
F
heard from that quaint lit - tle
he, and it's sim - ple to
C7
1.
bird who re - peat - ed one
see that the

Cuckoo! Cuckoo!
Let's waltz to a melody.
Cuckoo! Cuckoo!
As simple as it can be.
Cuckoo! Cuckoo!
We'll dance till the break of day.
Cuckoo!
Look who has stolen my heart away!

Sweet is the song that I heard
From that quaint little bird,
Who repeated one word.
He was cuckoo,
And I am as cuckoo as he,
And it's simple to see,
That the reason is you.
Cuckoo!

A simple song with opportunities for adding sound effects.

Summertime (Lullaby)

(from *Porgy And Bess*)

By George Gershwin,
Dubose and Dorothy Heyward
and Ira Gershwin

1 Summertime, an' the livin' is easy,
Fish are jumpin', and the cotton is high.
Oh, yo' daddy's rich, an' your ma is good lookin',
So, hush little baby, don't you cry.

2 One of these mornin's, you goin' to rise up singin',
Then you'll spread your wings, an' you'll take the sky,
But till that mornin', there's a-nothin' can harm you,
With Daddy an' Mammy standin' by.

A song that helps to portray the easy, relaxed feel of a hot summer's day.

The Green Leaves Of Summer

Words by Paul Francis Webster
Music by Dimitri Tiomkin

F7
B♭
Gm
3fr
Cm
3fr
sea - son of plen - ty, when the cat - fish were jump - in' as
C♯dim7
3fr
D
D7
high as the sky. A time just for plant - in', a
Gm
3fr
F7
B♭
Cm
3fr
time just for plough - in', a time to be court - in' a
A7
D
G7
Cm
3fr
girl of your own. T'was so good to be young then, to be

A time to be reapin',
A time to be sowin',
The green leaves of summer
Are callin' me home.

It was good to be young then,
In the season of plenty,
When the catfish were jumpin'
As high as the sky.

A time just for plantin',
A time just for ploughin',
A time to be courtin'
A girl of your own.

T'was so good to be young then,
To be close to the earth,
And to stand by your wife
At the moment of birth.

A good movement and action song.

Summer Holiday

Words and Music by
Bruce Welch and B Bennett

Medium rock

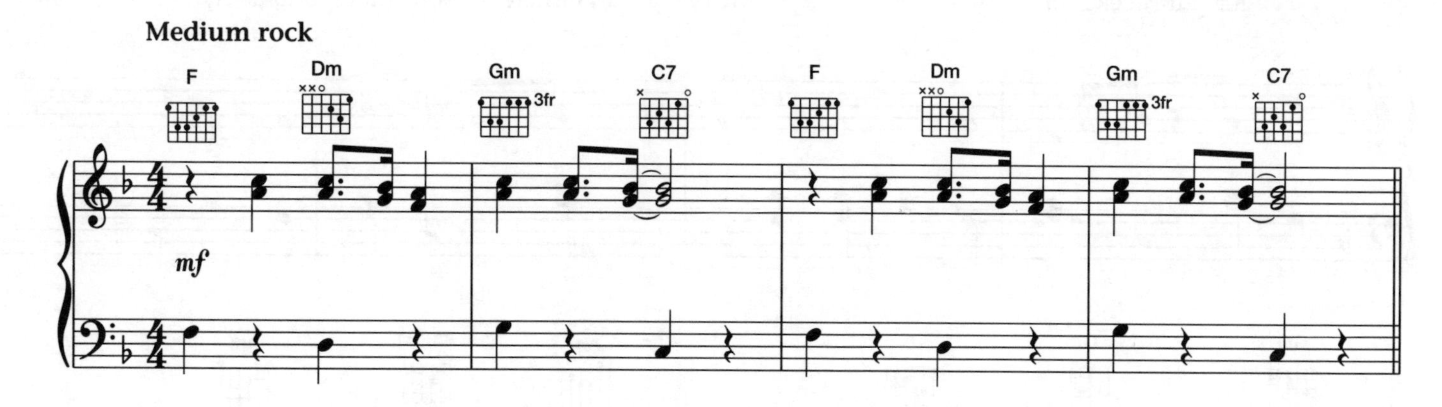

Gm
C7
F
Gm
C7
F
for a week_ or two. We're go - ing where the sun shines bright - ly, we're
Gm
C7
F
Am
Am/G#
Am
go - ing where the sea_ is blue. We've seen it_ in the_ mov - ies, now
G7
C
F
Dm
Gm
C7
let's see if it's true. Ev - ery - bo - dy has a sum - mer ho - li-day,
F
Dm
Gm
C7
F
Dm
Gm
C7
do - in' things they al - ways want-ed to,_ so we're go - ing on a sum-mer ho - li-day

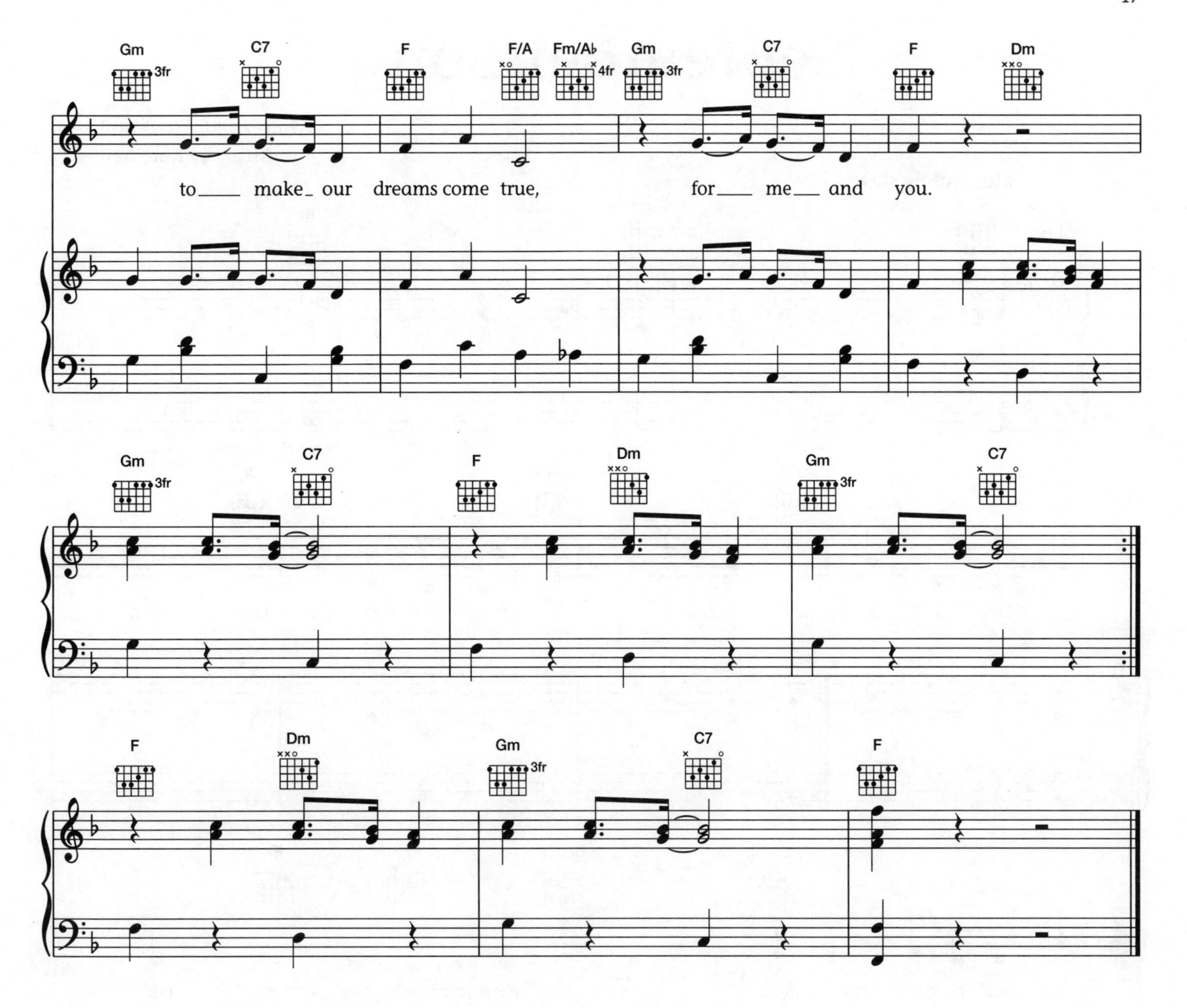

We're all going on a summer holiday,
No more working for a week or two,
Fun and laughter on our summer holiday,
No more worries for me or you,
For a week or two.

We're going where the sun shines brightly,
We're going where the sea is blue.
We've seen it in the movies,
Now let's see if it's true.

Everybody has a summer holiday,
Doin' things they always wanted to,
So we're going on a summer holiday,
To make our dreams come true,
For me and you.

A good thematic summer song, emphasising the leisurely side of the season.

September Song

Words by Maxwell Anderson
Music by Kurt Weill

C7
C7
F7
one has - n't got time for the wait - ing
B♭
E♭m
game. Oh, the days dwin-dle down to a
Edim7
E♭m
pre - cious few. Sep - tem - ber, No -
Edim7
B♭/F
B♭m
G♭/B♭
- vem - ber! And these few pre - cious days I'll spend with

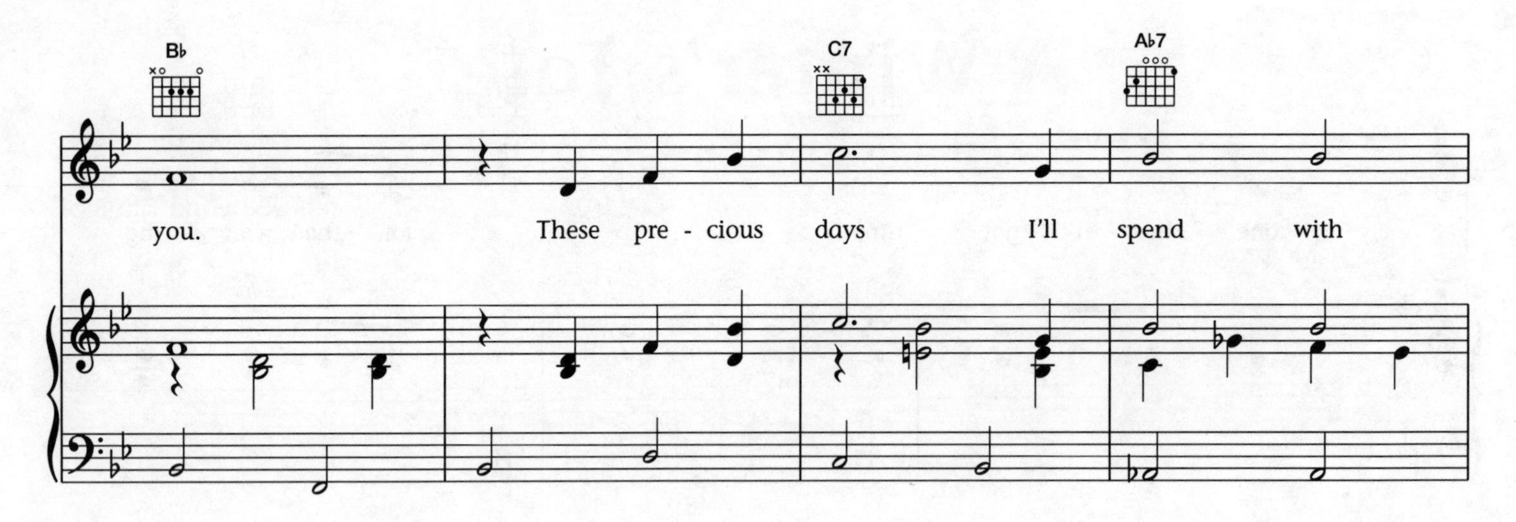

Oh, it's a long, long while
From May to December,
But the days grow short,
When you reach September.
When the autumn weather
Turns the leaves to flame,
One hasn't got time
For the waiting game.

Oh, the days dwindle down
To a precious few.
September,
November!
And these few precious days
I'll spend with you.
These precious days
I'll spend with you.

A taste of autumn in this song.

A Winter's Tale

Words and Music by
Mike Batt and Tim Rice

B♭/F
Am
B♭
night, my mem-or - ies are warm and clear, but ev - ery - bo - dy
well, for all that wish-es may be worth. I hope that love and
F
C/G
B♭
C7
F
knows it's hard to be a - lone at this time of year.
strength are with you for the length of your time on earth.
C7/G
F/A
It was on - ly a win-ter's tale, just an - oth - er win-ter's tale,
B♭
F
B♭/F
F
B♭
F
and why should the world take no - tice of one more love that's

1 The nights are colder now,
Maybe I should close the door,
And anyway, the snow has covered all your footsteps,
And I can follow you no more.
The fire still burns at night,
My memories are warm and clear,
But everybody knows it's hard to be alone
At this time of year.

It was only a winter's tale,
Just another winter's tale,
And why should the world take notice
Of one more love that's failed?
It's a love that can never be,
Though it meant a lot to you and me.
On a worldwide scale,
We're just another winter's tale.

2 While I stand alone,
A bell is ringing far away,
I wonder if you hear,
I wonder if you're listening,
I wonder where are you today?
Good luck! I wish you well,
For all that wishes may be worth.
I hope that love and strength are with you
For the length of your time on earth.
It was only ...

An alternative song for Christmas time.

The Twelve Days Of Christmas

Traditional

F/A Bb F/C C7 F Bb/F F F F/A Gm/Bb C7 F
par - tridge in a pear tree. 3. On the third day of Christ-mas my true love sent to me,
C7 C7 F/A Bb F/C C7 F Bb/F F
three french hens, two tur - tle doves, and a par - tridge in a pear tree. 4. On the
F F/A Gm/Bb C7 F C7
fourth day of Christ - mas my true love sent to me, four call - ing birds,
F/A Bb F/C C7
three french_ hens, two tur - tle doves, and a par - tridge_ in a pear

F Bb/F F F F/A Gm/Bb C7 F
tree. 5. On the fifth day of Christ - mas my true love sent to me,
F/A G7 C7 F/A Bb F/A
five gold rings, four calling birds, three french hens,
Gm/Bb Gm 3fr C C7/Bb F/A Bb F/C C7 F Bb/F F
two tur - tle doves, and a par - tridge in a pear tree.
6. On the
7. On the
8. On the
9. On the
F F/A Gm/Bb C7 F
1.
C7
sixth day of Christ - mas my true love sent to me, six geese a - lay - ing,
seventh day of Christ - mas my true love sent to me,
eighth day of Christ - mas my true love sent to me,
ninth day of Christ - mas my true love sent to me,

2.
C7
3.
C7
sev - en swans a - swim-ming, six geese a - lay - ing, eight maids a - milk - ing,
4.
C7
sev - en swans a - swim-ming, six geese a - lay - ing, nine la - dies danc - ing,
eight maids a - milk - ing, sev - en swans a - swim-ming, six geese a - lay - ing,
F/A
G7
C7
F/A
B♭
F/A
five gold rings, four call - ing birds, three french hens,

Gm/B♭ Gm 3fr C C7/B♭ F/A B♭ F/C C7 F B♭/F F
two___ tur - tle doves, and a par - tridge_ in a pear tree.
10. On the
11. On the
12. On the
F F/A Gm/B♭ C7 F C7
tenth day of Christ - mas my true love sent to me, ten lords a - leap - ing,
eleventh day of Christ - mas my true love sent to me, eleven pip - ers pip - ing,
twelfth day of Christ - mas my true love sent to me, twelve drum-mers drum-ming,

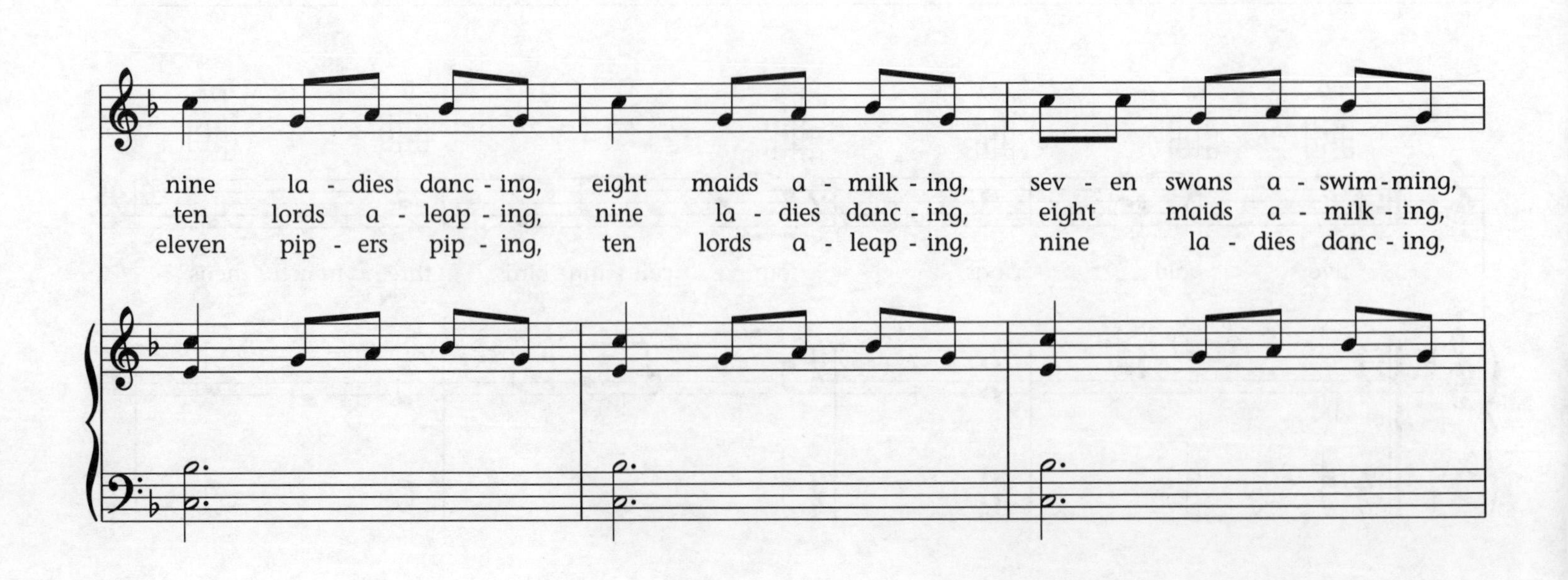
nine la - dies danc - ing, eight maids a - milk - ing, sev - en swans a - swim - ming,
ten lords a - leap - ing, nine la - dies danc - ing, eight maids a - milk - ing,
eleven pip - ers pip - ing, ten lords a - leap - ing, nine la - dies danc - ing,

Reproduced and printed by
Halstan & Co. Ltd., Amersham, Bucks., England

1 On the first day of Christmas,
My true love sent to me,
A partridge in a pear tree.

2 On the second day of Christmas,
My true love sent to me,
Two turtle doves,
And a partridge in a pear tree.

3 On the third day of Christmas,
My true love sent to me,
Three french hens,
Two turtle doves,
And a partridge in a pear tree.

4 On the fourth day of Christmas,
My true love sent to me,
Four calling birds,
Three french hens,
Two turtle doves,
And a partridge in a pear tree.

5 On the fifth day of Christmas,
My true love sent to me,
Five gold rings,
Four calling birds,
Three french hens,
Two turtle doves,
And a partridge in a pear tree.

6 On the sixth day of Christmas,
My true love sent to me,
Six geese a-laying,
Five gold rings,
Four calling birds,
Three french hens,
Two turtle doves,
And a partridge in a pear tree.

7 On the seventh day of Christmas,
My true love sent to me,
Seven swans a-swimming,
Six geese a-laying,
Five gold rings,
Four calling birds,
Three french hens,
Two turtle doves,
And a partridge in a pear tree.

8 On the eighth day of Christmas,
My true love sent to me,
Eight maids a-milking,
Seven swans a-swimming,
Six geese a-laying,
Five gold rings,
Four calling birds,
Three french hens,
Two turtle doves,
And a partridge in a pear tree.

9 On the ninth day of Christmas,
My true love sent to me,
Nine ladies dancing,
Eight maids a-milking,
Seven swans a-swimming,
Six geese a-laying,
Five gold rings,
Four calling birds,
Three french hens,
Two turtle doves,
And a partridge in a pear tree.

10 On the tenth day of Christmas,
My true love sent to me,
Ten lords a-leaping,
Nine ladies dancing,
Eight maids a-milking,
Seven swans a-swimming,
Six geese a-laying,
Five gold rings,
Four calling birds,
Three french hens,
Two turtle doves,
And a partridge in a pear tree.

11 On the eleventh day of Christmas,
My true love sent to me,
Eleven pipers piping,
Ten lords a-leaping,
Nine ladies dancing,
Eight maids a-milking,
Seven swans a-swimming,
Six geese a-laying,
Five gold rings,
Four calling birds,
Three french hens,
Two turtle doves,
And a partridge in a pear tree.

12 On the twelfth day of Christmas,
My true love sent to me,
Twelve drummers drumming,
Eleven pipers piping,
Ten lords a-leaping,
Nine ladies dancing,
Eight maids a-milking,
Seven swans a-swimming,
Six geese a-laying,
Five gold rings,
Four calling birds,
Three french hens,
Two turtle doves,
And a partridge in a pear tree.

**A popular festive song with lots of ideas for actions and cross-curricular links.
Try dividing the children into groups.**